Richard Addinsell

Warsaw Concerto

——

for Piano and Orchestra

Orchestral Reduction for Piano II by
PERCY ALDRIDGE GRAINGER

chappell/intersong
music group–usa

EXCLUSIVELY DISTRIBUTED BY

HAL•LEONARD®
CORPORATION

7777 W. BLUEMOUND RD. P.O. BOX 13819 MILWAUKEE, WI 53213

To J. N. B.

WARSAW CONCERTO
by
RICHARD ADDINSELL
for Piano and Orchestra
(or for two pianos)

N. B. Expression marks and metronome speeds not within brackets are from the original full orchestral score.
Pedalling, fingering and all expression marks and metronome speeds appearing within brackets have been supplied by the editor.

The solo piano part edited and the orchestral accompaniment arranged for a second piano by
Percy Aldridge Grainger
(1946)
By permission of G. Schirmer, Inc. N.Y.

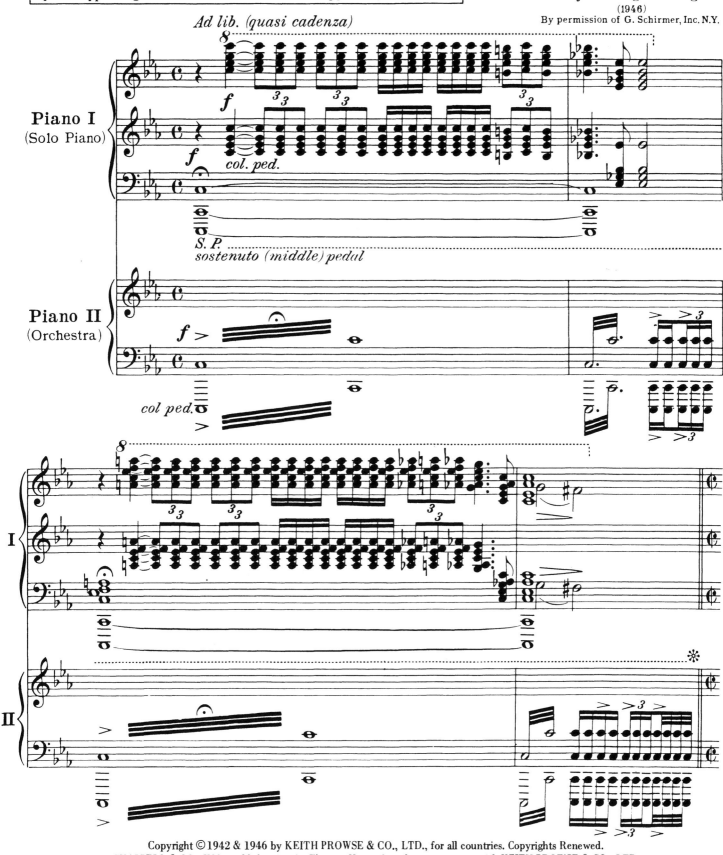

4

Allegro, ♩ = 108.

* When the Solo Piano plays with orchestra only the large notes should be played.
In performances by two pianos all the notes, large and small, should be played.

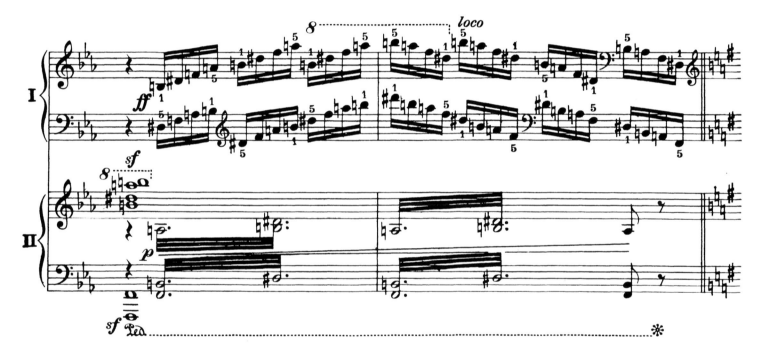

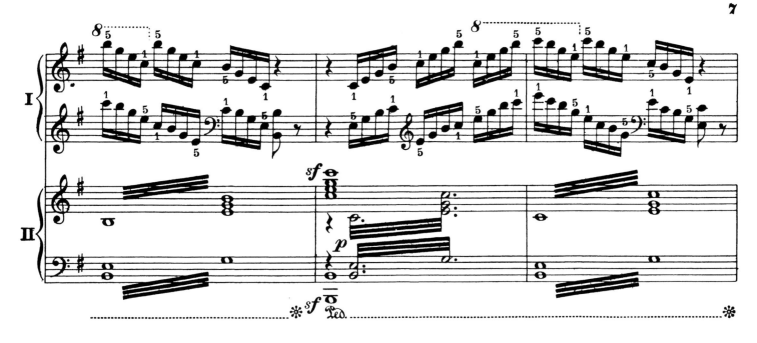

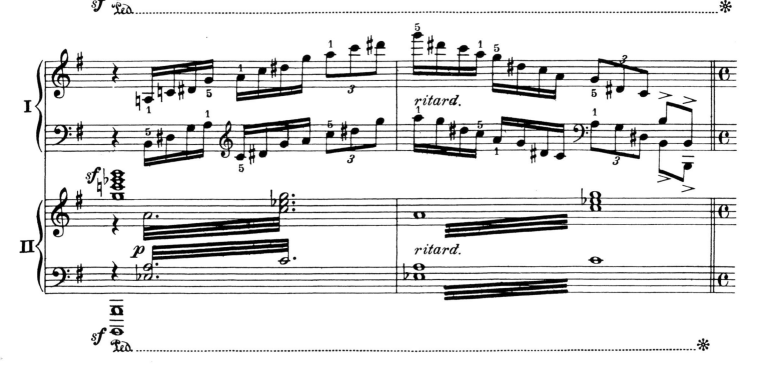

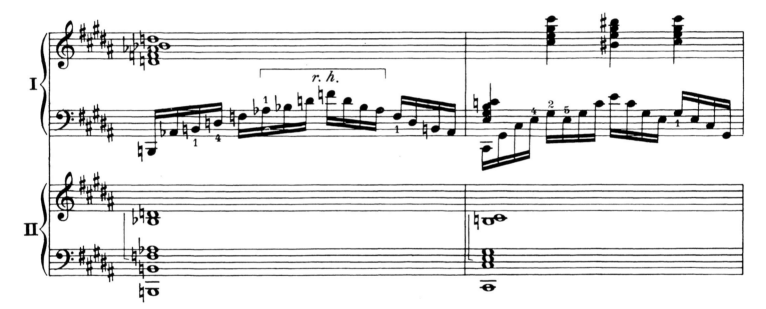

N.B. Easier (suggested by editor)

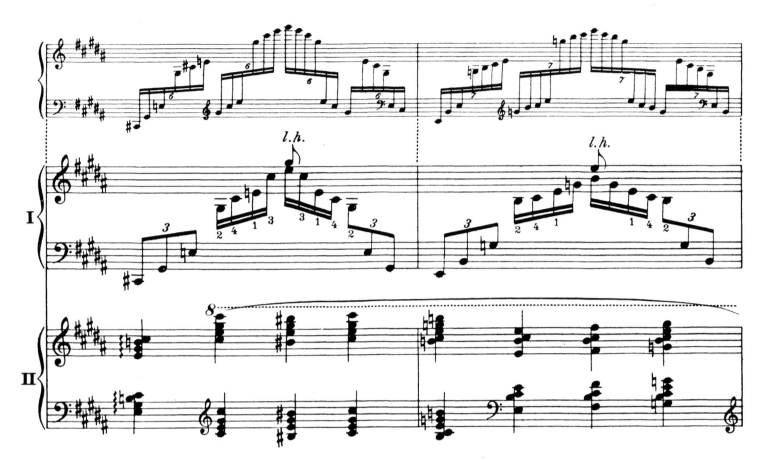

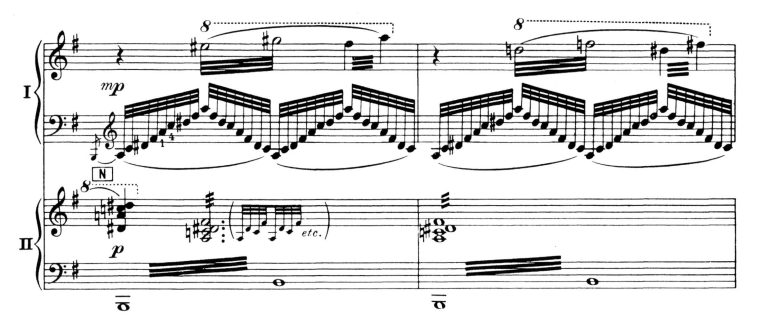

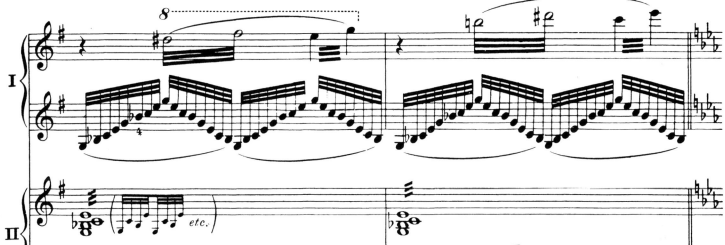

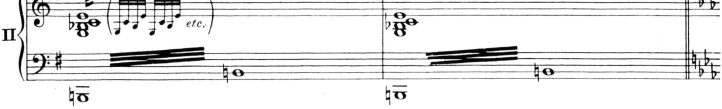

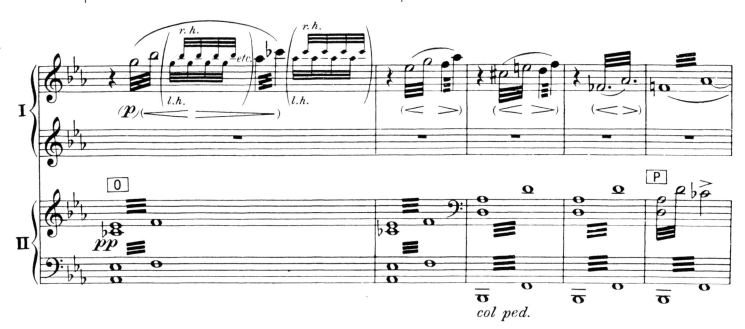

poco a poco accel. e cresc.

N.B. Division of hands suggested by editor

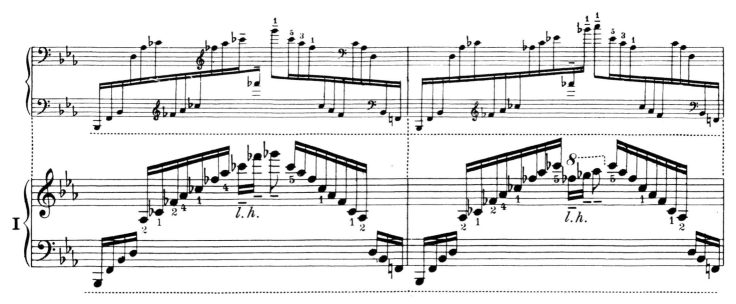

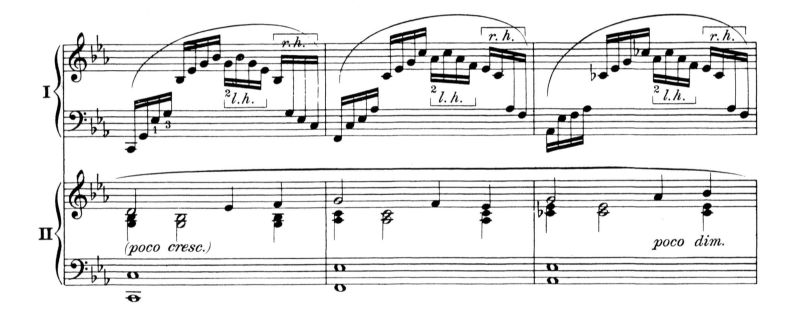

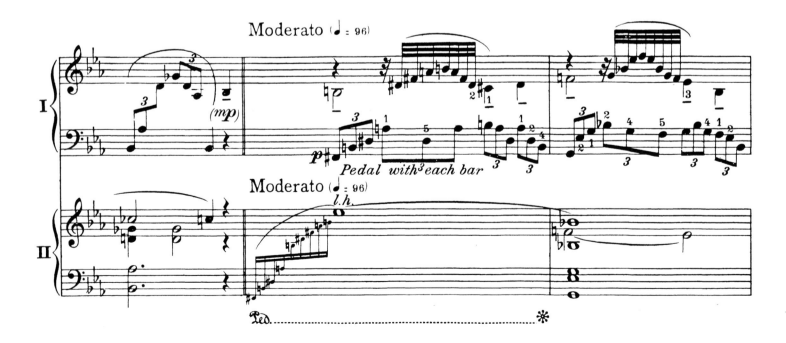

Pedal with each bar

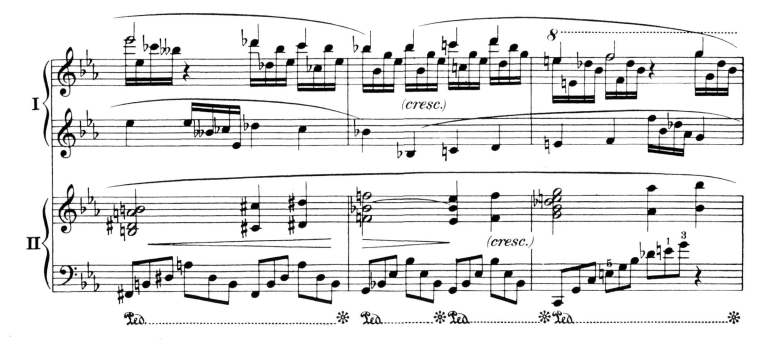

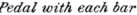

Pedal with each bar

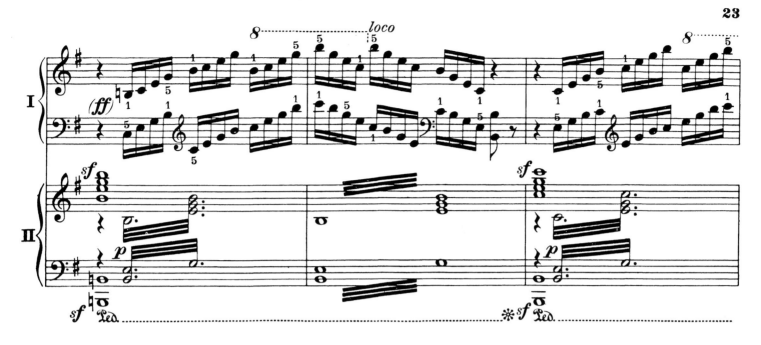

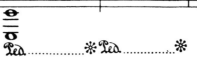

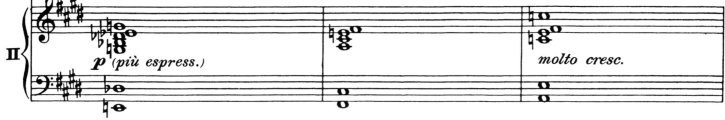

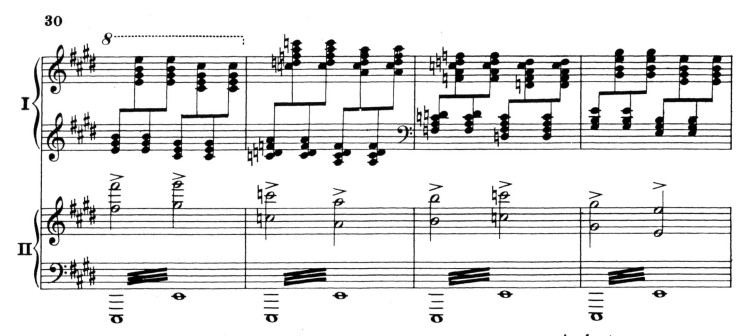

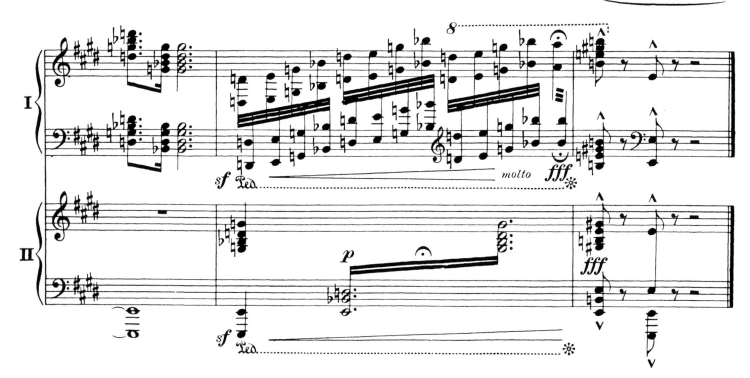